War of the Worlds

A graphic classic by
TOD OLSON AND TERRY WEST

Based on the novel by
H.G. WELLS

SCHOLASTIC INC.
New York Toronto London Auckland Sydney
Mexico City New Delhi Hong Kong Buenos Aires

Penciller/Layouts
Kalman Andrasofskzy

Colors, Inks, and Letters
Nimbus Studios

Cover Art
Phil Xavier and Nimbus Studios

Project Management
Greg Waller

7   8   9   10   23   12 11 10 09 08

H.G. Wells

(1866–1946)

In 1894, airplanes hadn't been invented. No one had been to the moon. And no one had dreamed about sending rockets to Mars. But a 28-year-old schoolteacher named H.G. Wells was already starting to imagine these developments.

That year, Mars came particularly close to Earth. An Italian astronomer announced that he'd seen "channels" there. People thought he meant "canals." And everyone started wondering if there was life on Mars.

Four years later, Wells wrote *War of the Worlds* about a Martian invasion.

Wells soon became famous for predicting the future. In *War of the Worlds*, he dreamed up industrial robots, laser weapons, and the use of poison gas in war. In seven other science fiction novels, he imagined tanks, air attacks, and nuclear war. Most of his predictions have come true.

THERE WAS A TIME WHEN I FELT SAFE UNDER THE SKIES.

I HAD A GOOD JOB AT A LOCAL COLLEGE.

DETENTION
~Kenny Norman
~Sean Vincent
~Kevin Wallace
~Charles Adler

I HAD A WONDERFUL WIFE, ANNA. WE HAD A LOVELY HOME IN THE SUBURBS.

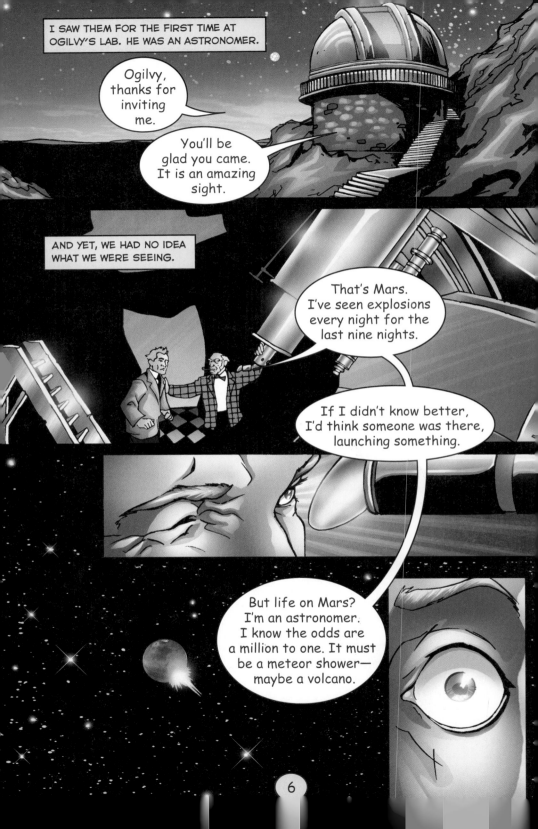

SEVERAL MORNINGS LATER, ANNA AND I WERE AWAKENED BY OGILVY.

One of those meteors we saw has fallen to Earth!

It's only five miles away. Get dressed, man!

IN 15 MINUTES, OGILVY AND I STOOD IN FRONT OF THE THING.

What on Earth!?

What on Earth!?

Ogilvy, could it really be from Mars?

It's certainly no meteor. And I've never seen anything like it on Earth.

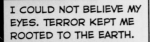

I COULD NOT BELIEVE MY EYES. TERROR KEPT ME ROOTED TO THE EARTH.

12

Oof!

NO!

IN SECONDS, THE MARTIANS UNLEASHED SOME KIND OF DEADLY RAY. HUMANITY HAD NEVER SEEN A WEAPON SO TERRIBLE.

NOTHING STOOD A CHANCE. TRUCKS WENT UP IN FLAMES.

THE SOLDIERS' GUNS WERE VAPORIZED.

FOR SOME REASON, I WAS LUCKIER THAN MOST. I SURVIVED.

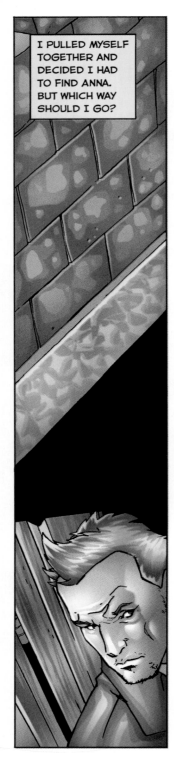

I PULLED MYSELF TOGETHER AND DECIDED I HAD TO FIND ANNA. BUT WHICH WAY SHOULD I GO?

I DECIDED TO HEAD INTO THE CITY WHERE MY BROTHER LIVED. I THOUGHT ANNA MIGHT HAVE GONE THERE.

Could she possibly still be alive?

FOR TWO DAYS, I WAS ON THE RUN WHILE THE MARTIANS ADVANCED.

FEAR WAS QUICKLY TURNING US ALL INTO ANIMALS.

Please, sir, we need a ride.

Get away!

Out of my way!

Help!

TRYING TO FLEE THE MARTIANS, PEOPLE TRAMPLED THEIR FELLOW HUMAN BEINGS.

THEY BECAME CRIMINALS IN ORDER TO SURVIVE.

Hurry up! They might be coming back.

POOR OGILVY HAD HINTED AT THE ANSWER TO THE FIRST QUESTION THAT NIGHT IN THE OBSERVATORY.

"... MARS IS GETTING COLDER BY THE MINUTE ...

"... IF THERE WAS EVER LIFE THERE, IT IS FROZEN BY NOW."

I SUDDENLY KNEW THE ANSWER TO MY FIRST QUESTION.

THEY HAD COME HERE SO THEIR RACE WOULD SURVIVE.

THE SECOND QUESTION WAS ANSWERED BY THE MARTIANS THEMSELVES ...

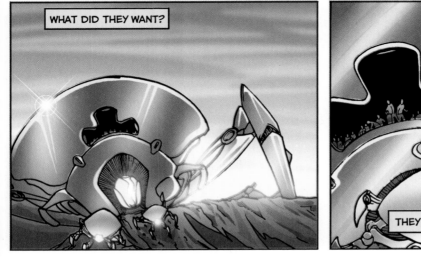

WHAT DID THEY WANT?

THEY WANTED *US*.

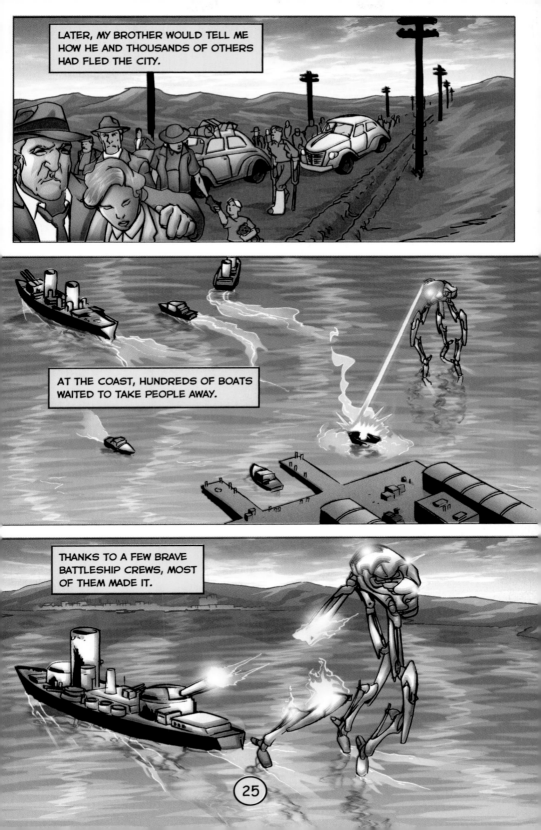

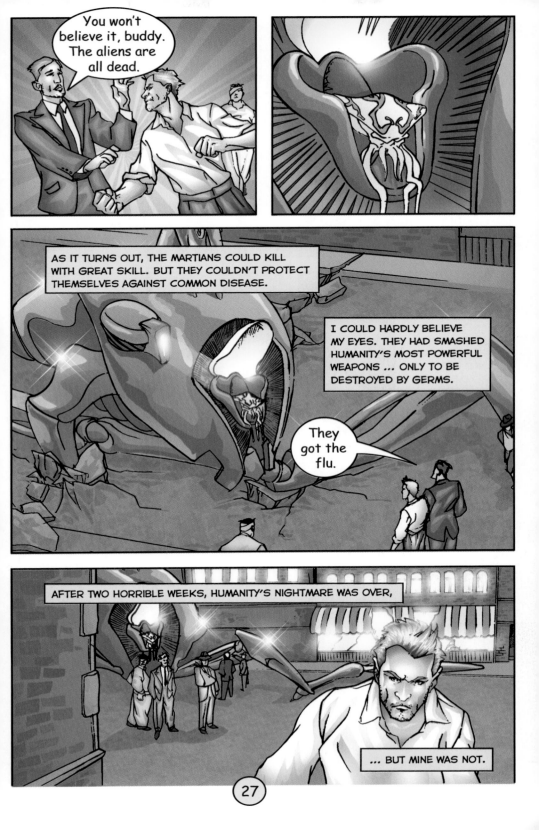